The Joy of New Pop Hits

CW00350674

This publication is not authorised for sale in
the United States of America and / or Canada

Wise Publications
part of The Music Sales Group
London / New York / Paris / Sydney / Copenhagen / Berlin / Madrid / Tokyo

Published by
Wise Publications
8/9 Frith Street, London W1D 3JB, England.

Exclusive Distributors:
Music Sales Limited
Distribution Centre, Newmarket Road, Bury St. Edmunds, Suffolk IP33 3YB, England.
Music Sales Pty Limited
120 Rothschild Avenue, Rosebery, NSW 2018, Australia.

Order No. AM977240
ISBN 1-84449-040-8
This book © Copyright 2003 by Wise Publications.

Unauthorised reproduction of any part of this publication by
any means including photocopying is an infringement of copyright.

Edited by Sarah Holcroft.
Music arranged by Richard Blair Oliphant.
Music processed by Enigma Music Production Services.
Cover illustration by Arlene Adams.
Printed in the United Kingdom by Caligraving Limited, Thetford, Norfolk.

Your Guarantee of Quality
As publishers, we strive to produce every book to the highest commercial standards.
The music has been freshly engraved and the book has been carefully designed to
minimise awkward page turns and to make playing from it a real pleasure.
Particular care has been given to specifying acid-free, neutral-sized paper made from
pulps which have not been elemental chlorine bleached.
This pulp is from farmed sustainable forests and was produced with special regard for the environment.
Throughout, the printing and binding have been planned to ensure a sturdy,
attractive publication which should give years of enjoyment.
If your copy fails to meet our high standards, please inform us and we will gladly replace it.

www.musicsales.com

All The Things She Said

Words & Music by Sergei Galoyan, Trevor Horn,
Martin Kierszenbaum, Elena Kiper & Valerij Polienko

All the things she said, all the things she said, run-ning through my

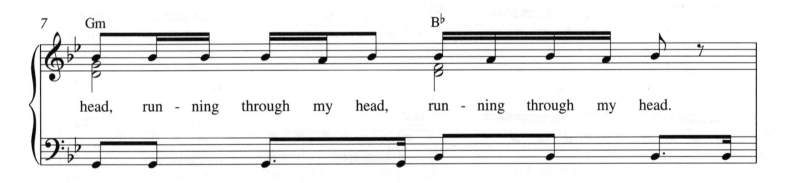

head, run-ning through my head, run-ning through my head.

All the things she said, all the things she said, run-ning through my

© Copyright 2002 Appleby Music/BMG Music Publishing Limited (25%)/Unforgettable Songs Limited (25%)/

Universal Music Publishing Limited (8.34%)/Copyright Control (41.66%).

All Rights Reserved. International Copyright Secured.

Beautiful

Words & Music by Linda Perry

(Don't look at me)   Vocal ad lib.

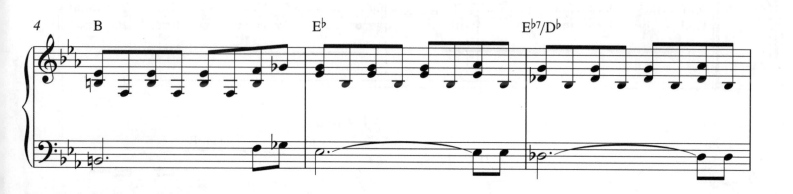

1. Ev-'ry day___ is so
2. To all your friends_ you're de-

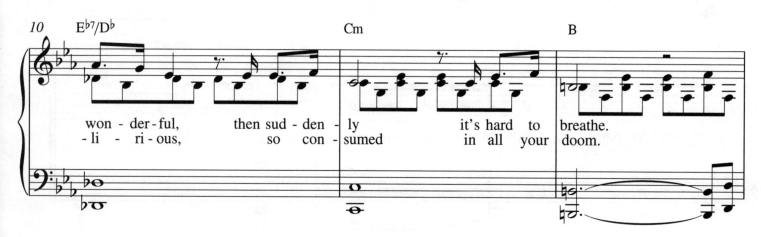

won-der-ful,   then sud-den-ly   it's hard to breathe.
-li-ri-ous,   so con-sumed   in all your doom.

© Copyright 2001 Famous Music Corporation, USA.

All Rights Reserved. International Copyright Secrued.

And ev-'ry where we go,_____ the sun will al-ways shine,_

but to-mor-row we might a-wake,___ on___ the oth-er side._

D.S. al Coda

Coda

- day.

Vocal ad lib.

Free time

Don't you bring me down to-day.

Born To Try

Words & Music by Delta Goodrem & Audius Mtawarira

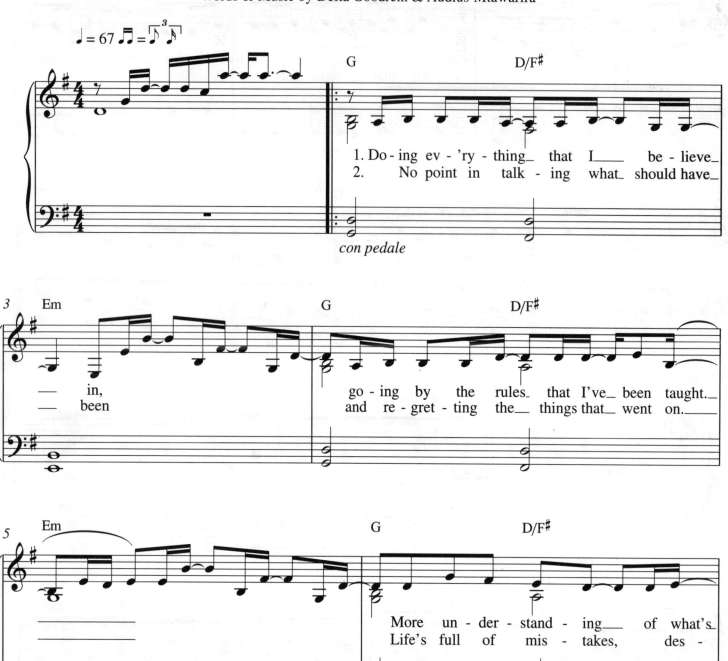

1. Do-ing ev-'ry-thing that I__ be-lieve
2. No point in talk-ing what__ should have__

__ in,
__ been

go-ing by the rules__ that I've__ been taught.__
and re-gret-ting the__ things that__ went on.__

__ a-round me__
-ti-nies and__ fates.__

More un-der-stand-ing__ of what's
Life's full of mis-takes, des-

and pro-tec-ted__ from the walls__
Re-move the clouds, look at the big-

© Copyright 2003 Sony Music Publishing Australia PTY.

Sony/ATV Music Publishing (UK) Limited.

All Rights Reserved. International Copyright Secured.

Clocks

Words & Music by Guy Berryman, Jon Buckland, Will Champion & Chris Martin

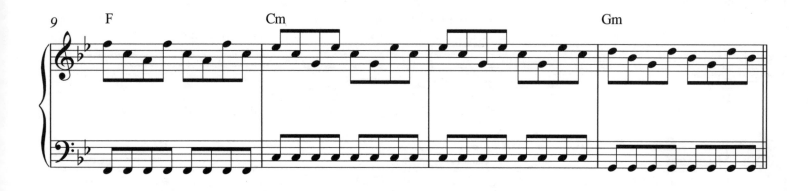

1. Lights go out and I can't be saved,___ tides that I tried to
2. Con - fus - ion that nev - er stops,___ clos - ing walls and

© Copyright 2002 BMG Music Publishing Limited.
All Rights Reserved. International Copyright Secured.

Come Undone

Words & Music by Robbie Williams, Boots Ottestad, Ashley Hamilton & Daniel Pierre

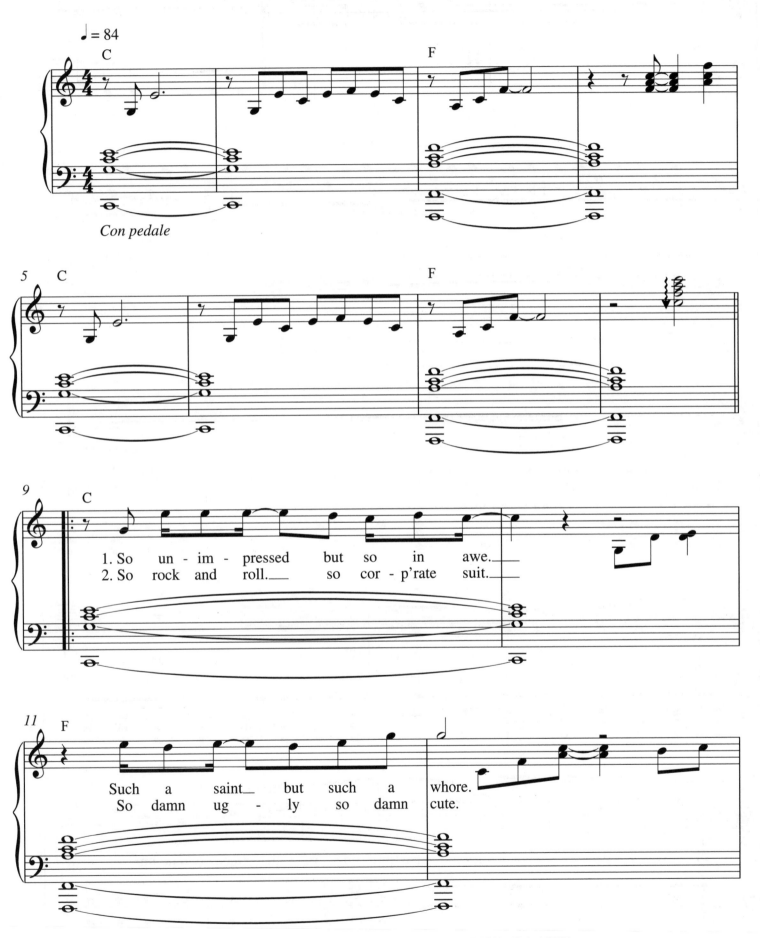

© Copyright 2002 BMG Music Publishing Limited (25%)/EMI Music Publishing Limited (50%)/
Twenty Seven Songs/RZO Music Limited (25%).
All Rights Reserved. International Copyright Secured.

So write a-no-ther bal-lad, mix it on a Wednes-day.

Sell it on a Thurs-day, buy a yacht by Sat-ur-day, it's a love____ song,_ a

love____ song.__ Do a-no-ther in-ter-view, sing a bunch of lies.

Tell a-bout ce-le-bri-ties that I des-pise__ and sing love____ songs. We sing

love____ songs, so sin-cere.

So sin-cere.

Cry Me A River

Words & Music by Justin Timberlake, Scott Storch & Tim Mosley

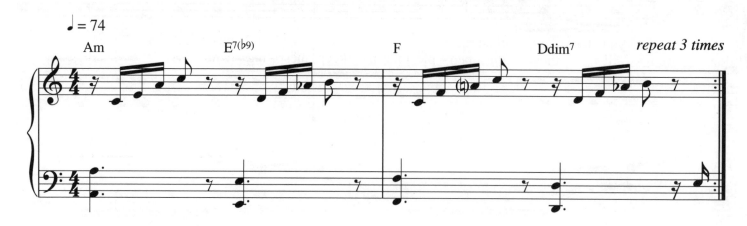

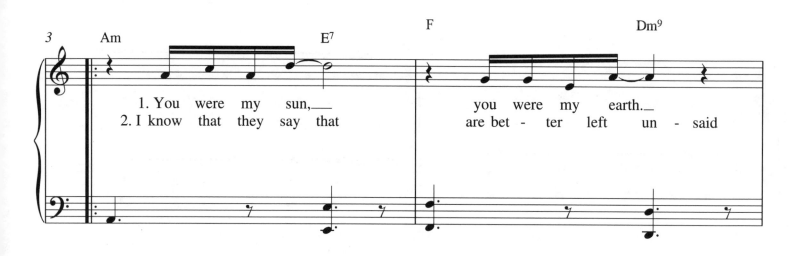

1. You were my sun,___ you were my earth.___
2. I know that they say that are bet - ter left un - said

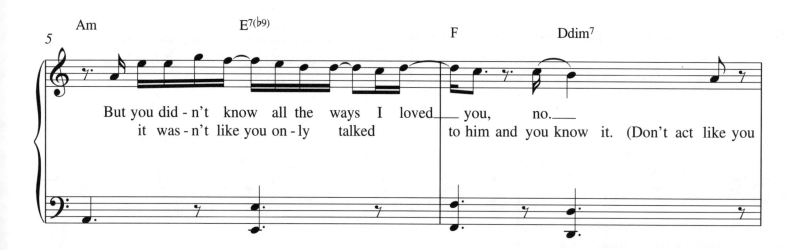

But you did - n't know all the ways I loved___ you, no.___
it was - n't like you on - ly talked to him and you know it. (Don't act like you

© Copyright 2002 Tennman Tunes/TVT Music Incorporated/Virginia Beach Music, USA.
EMI Music Publishing Limited (25%)/Warner/Chappell Music Limited (25%)/Zomba Music Publishers Limited (50%).
All Rights Reserved. International Copyright Secured.

Now there's just no chance for you and me, there'll nev-er be. Cry me a riv-

-er, cry me a riv - er girl. Cry me a riv - er, cry me a riv-

-er girl. Cry me a riv - er girl. Cry me a riv - er, cry me a riv-

Repeat ad lib. to fade

-er, oh, cry me a riv - er. Oh, cry me a riv - er. Oh, cry me a riv-

If You're Not The One

Words & Music by Daniel Bedingfield

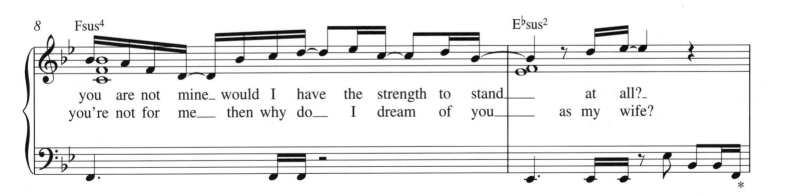

© Copyright 2002 Sony/ATV Music Publishing (UK) Limited.
All Rights Reserved. International Copyright Secured.

Little By Little

Words & Music by Noel Gallagher

© Copyright 2002 Oasis Music/Creation Songs Limited/Sony/ATV Music Publishing (UK) Limited.

All Rights Reserved. International Copyright Secured.

Love Doesn't Have To Hurt

Words & Music by Tom Kelly, Billy Steinberg & Susanna Hoffs

(Thank - you ba - by.)

1. I learned a les - son in my life,   but I learnt it the
2. Darl - ing now_ it seems to me   like I've al - ways_

hard   way.   I don't know why I used to fall in love
— known_ you.   But I still shud-der when I think back

© Copyright 1997 EMI Music Publishing Limited (70%)/Copyright Control (30%).
All Rights Reserved. International Copyright Secured.

with the wrong___ kind.
on the lone - ly___ times.

Then I'd
I used___ to

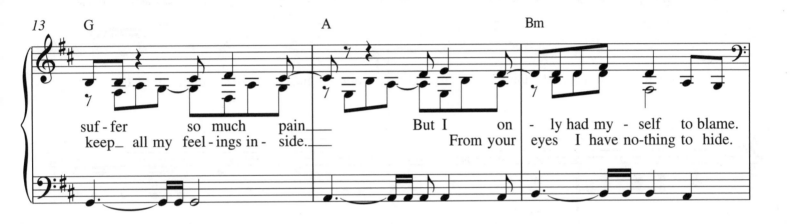

suf - fer   so much   pain___
keep___ all my feel - ings in - side.___

But I   on - ly had my - self   to blame.
From your eyes   I have no-thing to hide.

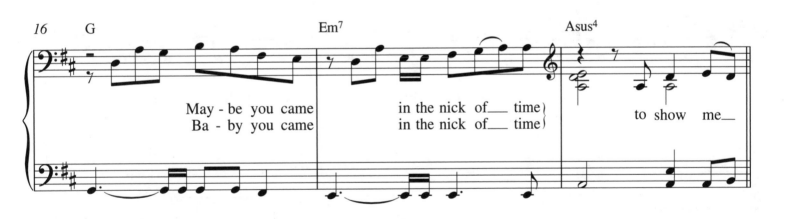

May - be you came
Ba - by you came

in the nick of___ time
in the nick of___ time

to show   me___

love does - n't have to hurt

to feel___ good.

It's

and al - ways should. Don't have_ to cry, don't have_ to fight,

and in__ your arms__ night af - ter night,__ you showed me

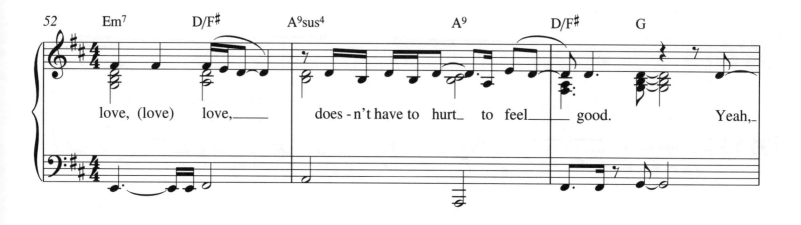

love, (love) love,___ does - n't have to hurt_ to feel___ good. Yeah,_

__ yeah. Thank - you ba - by. (Thank-you ba-by)

Shape

Words & Music by Sting, Dominic Miller, Craig Dodds,
Kenneth Dodds, Mutya Buena, Kiesha Buchanan, Heidi Range & Siobhan Donaghy

con pedale

1. I live my

life in chains, got my hands in chains and I
(2.) played it safe, no - thing's ev - er safe.

can't stick with the cards that I got with a deal like this.__ I must in -
Give me the cou - rage to back my own con - vic - tions.

© Copyright 2002 Steerpike Limited (42.5%)/Magnetic Publishing Limited (42.5%)/Copyright Control (6.75%)/
Ministry Of Sound Music Publishing Limited (6.75%)/EMI Music Publishing Limited (1%)/Universal Music Publishing Limited (0.5%).
All Rights Reserved. International Copyright Secured.

Spirit In The Sky

Words & Music by Norman Greenbaum

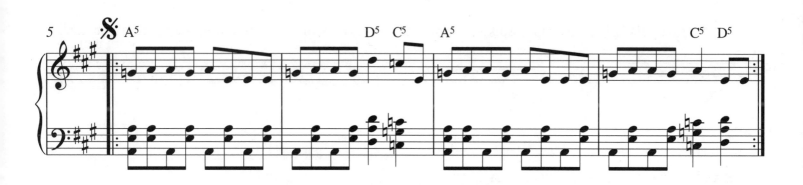

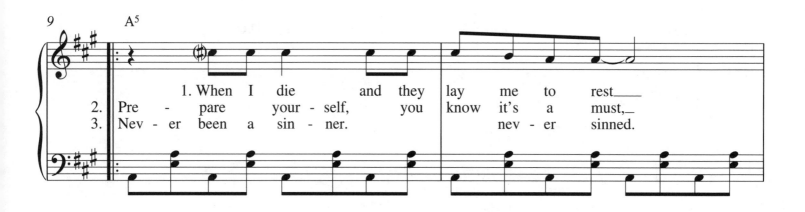

1. When I die and they lay me to rest____
2. Pre - pare your - self, you know it's a must,__
3. Nev - er been a sin - ner. nev - er sinned.

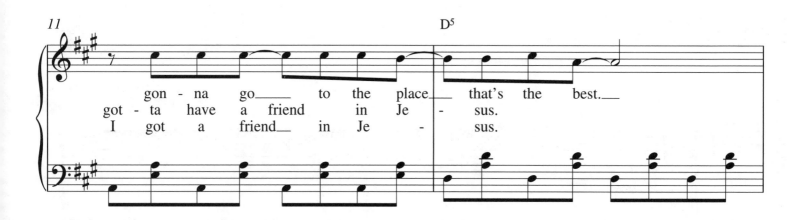

gon - na go____ to the place___ that's the best.__
got - ta have a friend in Je - sus.
I got a friend__ in Je - sus.

© Copyright 1969 & 1970 Great Honesty Music Incorporated, USA.

Westminster Music Limited.

All Rights Reserved. International Copyright Secured.

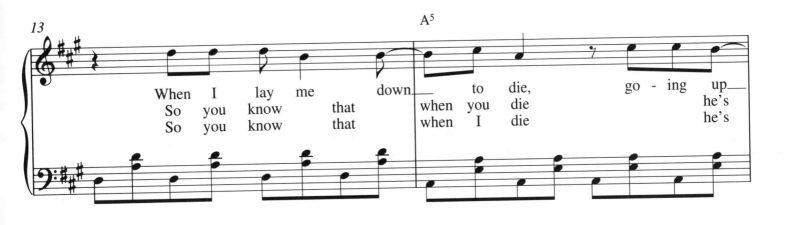

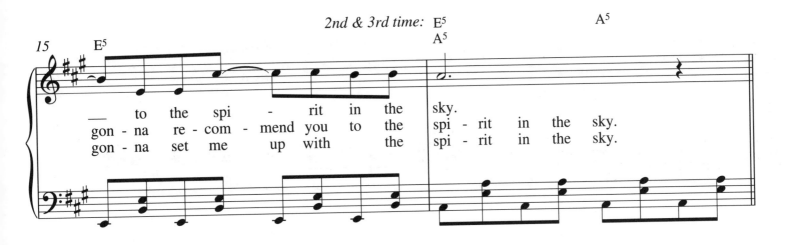

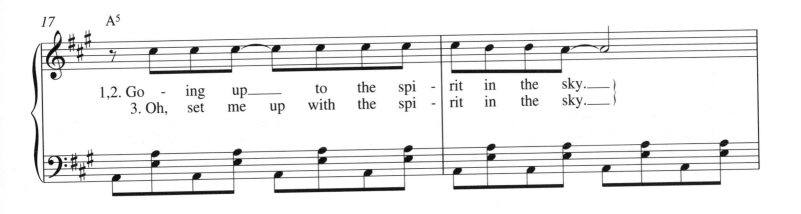

lay me to rest   I'm gon - na   go to the   place   that's the   best.

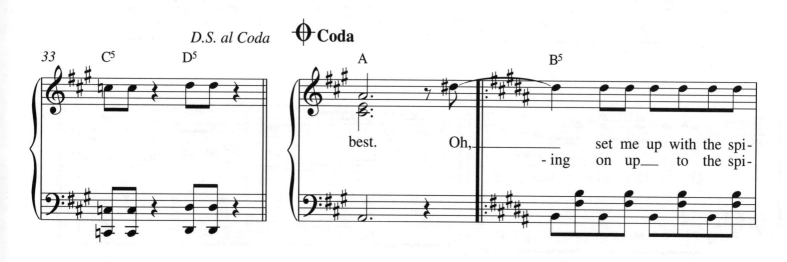

best.   Oh,_____   set me up with the spi-
                                    - ing   on up___ to the spi-

54

Tonight

Words & Music by Steve Mac, Wayne Hector & Jörgen Elofsson

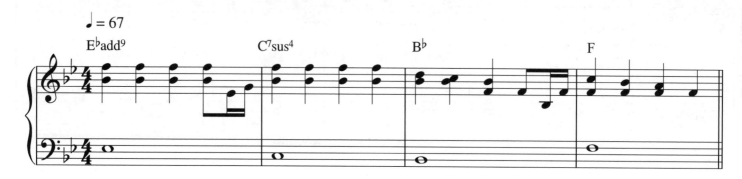

1. La - dy I'm so___ tired.   If I took it all___ out on
2. I don't wan - na act___ like   I know that you'll be___ mine for -

you.   I nev - er meant___ to.
-ever   though I won't wait for - ev - er.

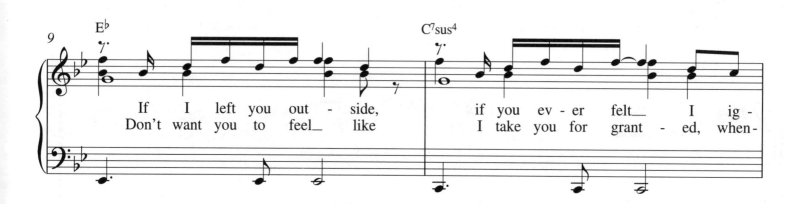

If I left you out - side,   if you ev - er felt___ I ig -
Don't want you to feel___ like   I take you for grant - ed, when-

© Copyright 2002 Rokstone Music (33.34%)/Universal Music Publishing Limited (33.33%)/BMG Music Publishing Limited (33.33%).
All Rights Reserved. International Copyright Secured.

U Make Me Wanna

Words & Music by John McLaughlin, Steve Robson & Harry Wilkins

1. To start it off I know you know me.
2. Well I know that these feel - ings won't end, no, no.

To come to think of it, it was on - ly last week that I had a dream a - bout us,
They get strong - er if I see you a - gain. Ba - by I'm tired of be -

© Copyright 2001 Windswept Music (London) Limited (33.34%)/
Rondor Music (London) Limited (33.33%)/Rumour Control Limited (33.33%).
All Rights Reserved. International Copyright Secured.